Lesson 1

When a word has 2 consonants that come between 2 vowels, the word is divided into syllables between the 2 consonants — vc/cv.

trum / pet

Draw a line between the syllables in each word below:

bon|net	object
absent	connect
chapter	wisdom
publish	plastic
expect	droplet

Read, write, and "X" it:

1. lesson _lesson_			
2. gallop _____			
3. pretzel _____			
4. rubbish _____			
5. blossom _____			
6. helmet _____			
7. album _____			

When a word has 2 consonants that come between 2 vowels, the word is divided into syllables between the 2 consonants—vc/cv.

trum / pet

 it:

 whiskers or (whisper)?	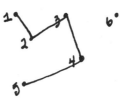 tunnel or tomcat?
 pepper or better?	 contest or connect?
  blossom or blister?	 padlock or piglet?
 tipping or temper?	 bottom or button?

		Spell:			Write:
1.		(gal) lag		lap (lop)	*gallop*
2.		dot bot		mot tom	_____
3.		in im		sect test	_____
4.		pop pep		per pen	_____
5.		al at		dum bum	_____
6.		cac cag		tus sut	_____
7.		kim ken		mal nel	_____

Explode The Code 4 ½

Nancy Hall
Rena Price

EDUCATORS PUBLISHING SERVICE
Cambridge and Toronto

CONTENTS

Cover Design by Hugh Price
Text illustrations by Andrew Mockler

Printed in U.S.A.
ISBN 0-8388-1777-7
978-0-8388-1777-3

8 9 10 11 CUR 10 09 08 07

Yes or No?

		Yes	No
1.	Can an insect fly as fast as a jet?	☐	☒
2.	Do you like to munch on a pretzel?	☐	☐
3.	Will she need a helmet to play with a kitten?	☐	☐
4.	Can a ribbon be put on a box top?	☐	☐
5.	Would you like to eat a cactus for supper?	☐	☐
6.	Does pepper help a blossom grow?	☐	☐
7.	Should they pick up rubbish after the picnic?	☐	☐

To help read these words, think of the rules to divide words into syllables.

◯ the word to match the picture:

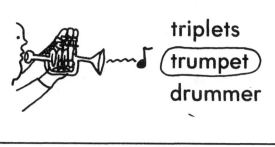

triplets
(trumpet)
drummer

whether
whisker
whisper

hamlet
helmet
helper

blossom
bottom
box top

invent
insult
invite

catnip
catsup
cactus

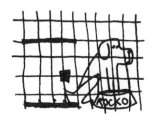

kettle
kennel
nickel

unsafe
impact
insect

6

Pick the best word to finish each sentence:

lesson	gallop	~~bottom~~
album	insects	helmet
kennel	whisper	cactus

1. A box has a top and a ___*bottom*___.

2. Lots of dogs can stay in a _____.

3. If you grab a _____, it may prick you.

4. The class will try to do a _____ each day.

5. He should use a _____ when he rides his bike on the street.

6. A bee, a fly, and an ant are _____.

7. Babe likes to ride and _____ fast on her mare.

"X" it:

1.	The drummer has a temper tantrum. ☐ The drummer plays the silver trumpet. ☒	
2.	The tomcat dives for the pretzel. ☐ The tomcat drives with a helmet. ☐	
3.	Pepper whines in his kennel. ☐ The padlock on the kennel is rusted. ☐	
4.	The insect sits in the bottom of the glass. ☐ Ellen inspects the glass-bottomed boat. ☐	
5.	Dot dumps the old album in the rubbish. ☐ Dot hates to take her old rocker to the dump. ☐	
6.	The rabbit whispers its plan to the cactus. ☐ The rabbit's whiskers tickle the catfish. ☐	
7.	The monster is singing for its supper. ☐ My sister acts like a monster when she is swimming. ☐	

8

Write it:

1.		_helmet_ _____
2.		_____
3.		_____
4.		_____
5.		_____
6.		_____
7.		_____

When 1 consonant stands between 2 vowels, the word is usually divided after the first vowel — v/cv. The first syllable is **open**, and the vowel says its name.

hō / tĕl

Draw a line between the syllables so that the first vowel says its name:

lilac	crisis
event	locate
spoken	depend
prefer	shaving
elect	pretend

Read, write, and "X" it:

1.	Friday _____			
2.	siren _____			
3.	begin _____			
4.	Cupid _____			
5.	hero _____			
6.	spider _____			
7.	driver _____			

When 1 consonant stands between 2 vowels, the word is usually divided after the first vowel—v/cv. The first syllable is **open**, and the vowel says its name.

hō / tĕl

◯ it:

beaver or fever?

hello or halo?

demon or demand?

relax or relay?

omit or over?

hemlock or hero?

solo or sofa?

trading or frozen?

	Spell:		Write:
1.	sip spi	per der	_____
2.	ha na	to lo	_____
3.	cov clo	ver ner	_____
4.	pap pu	al pil	_____
5.	ba da	sin um	_____
6.	o a	pam pen	_____
7.	sin si	ren ner	_____

Yes or No?

	Yes	No
1. Can you relax and sleep late on Friday?	☐	☐
2. If you have a fever, do you feel frozen?	☐	☐
3. Will a driver go faster when she hears a siren?	☐	☐
4. Will you have good luck if you find a 4-leaf clover?	☐	☐
5. Is it fun for a pupil to begin *Explode The Code*?	☐	☐
6. Does Cupid have a bow and arrow?	☐	☐
7. If you are a hero, will you have a halo?	☐	☐

To help read these words, think of the rules to divide words into syllables.

 the word to match the picture:

even
oval
open

finest
Friday
frozen

hotel
motor
hating

silent
silo
siren

demand
David
Danish

basin
basal
basis

consent
clatter
clover

hello
halo
haven

15

Pick the best word to finish each sentence:

Friday	open	clover
begin	relax	hotel
hero	basin	siren

1. If he helps save a life, he is a _____.

2. In the grass you may find green _____.

3. I use soap to clean my hands in the _____.

4. _____ is a day that comes each week.

5. It is fun to _____ and chat with a pal.

6. On a trip you may stop and sleep at a _____.

7. You close a gate if you do not want it _____.

"X" it:

1. The spider will relax and swing in its hammock. ☐

   Miss Muffet thinks the spider is a hero. ☐

2. David will open the can and feed Simon. ☐

   Simon invites David over on Friday. ☐

3. Cupid is picking clover in the grass. ☐

   Clover is sticking to Cupid's bow. ☐

4. The driver stopped when the siren began. ☐

   The siren on my motorbike is not legal. ☐

5. Susan demands a frozen treat on the hot day. ☐

   Susan's feet are frozen in her sandals. ☐

6. The pupil with the fever must stay in bed. ☐

   Hazel will see if the insect has a fever. ☐

7. Jake is singing a solo at the hotel. ☐

   Jane is washing in the basin at the hotel. ☐

Write it:

#		
1.		_____
2.		_____
3.		_____
4.		_____
5.		_____
6.		_____
7.		_____

Lesson 3

When a word has 1 consonant between 2 vowels, sometimes the word is divided **after** the consonant—vc/v.
The first syllable is now **closed**, and the vowel is short.

rŏb / in

Draw a line between the syllables so that the first vowel is short:

exact	panel
habit	credit
famish	satin
modest	sliver
topic	denim

Read, write, and "X" it:

1.	camel _____			
2.	dozen _____			
3.	timid _____			
4.	closet _____			
5.	exit _____			
6.	comet _____			
7.	visit _____			

When a word has 1 consonant between 2 vowels, sometimes the word is divided after the consonant—vc/v. The first syllable is now closed, and the vowel is short.

rŏb / in

◯ it:

 travel or gravel?	 over or oven?
 rebel or pedal?	 frolic or frozen?
 tonic or talent?	 sliver or shiver?
 timid or limit?	 venom or melon?

	Spell:			Write:
1.	com	clos	el	et	_____
2.	vis	vit	sor	it	_____
3.	sic	sec	nod	ond	_____
4.	ok	ex	it	at	_____
5.	riv	rim	en	er	_____
6.	rab	rad	ding	ish	_____
7.	mel	nal	on	am	_____

22

Yes or No?

		Yes	No
1.	Would you like to eat a dozen melons?	☐	☐
2.	Do robins visit us in the spring?	☐	☐
3.	Is it clever to pedal your bike in the mud?	☐	☐
4.	If you can make a model train, do you have talent?	☐	☐
5.	When you shiver in bed, should you pull up the covers?	☐	☐
6.	Would you mix gravel with pudding and put it in the oven?	☐	☐
7.	If there is a fire, will you go to the nearest exit?	☐	☐

To help read these words, think of the rules to divide words into syllables.

◯ the word to match the picture:

camel
clever
closet

secret
second
seven

robot
roping
robin

shiver
shaving
sliver

doses
dozen
dozing

clover
comet
cover

topaz
tropics
trapeze

river
rival
rover

Pick the best word to finish each sentence:

talent	visit	radish
oven	model	river
gravel	dozen	cover

1.

When you make a road, you may need _____.

2.

David puts a _____ on top of the pot.

3.

Twelve eggs make a _____.

4.

When you bake a cake, you put it in an _____.

5.

She likes to row the boat down the _____.

6.

It is fun to _____ a pal at her home.

7.

I like to put together a _____ of a plane.

"X" it:

1.
A dozen kids are on the bus when it has a flat. ☐

The bus driver has a dozen eggs in the backseat. ☐

2.
Janet has a talent for making models. ☐

Janet has a talent for growing melons. ☐

3.
The robin shivers as it waits for spring to begin. ☐

Robin shaves his beard before spring begins. ☐

4.
The river has lots of gravel on its bottom. ☐

Rover puts lots of grated cheese on his meatballs. ☐

5.
Duke will cover the melon with green soap. ☐

Grease from the oven covers Duke's pants. ☐

6.
The timid robin hopped over to the exit. ☐

The clever robber hoped to sneak in the exit. ☐

7.
Mabel hit the gas pedal and drove into the bike shop. ☐

When Mabel's bike tipped over, the pedal hit the gravel. ☐

26

Write it:

1. _____

2. _____

3. _____

4. _____

5. _____

6. _____

7. _____

27

Lesson 4

Each of these words has 1 consonant between 2 vowels.

1) If you divide after the first vowel, that vowel says its name:

pī / lot

2) If you divide after the consonant, the vowel is short:

prĕs / ent

Draw a line between the syllables to make a real word:

linen	moment
mimic	banish
demon	result
crisis	menu
limit	evil

28

Read, write, and "X" it:

1.	fever			
	_____			
2.	label			
	_____			
3.	sliver			
	_____			
4.	Jason			
	_____			
5.	prison			
	_____			
6.	shiver			
	_____			
7.	solid			
	_____			

Each of these words has 1 consonant between 2 vowels.

1) If you divide after the first vowel, that vowel says its name:

$$\text{pī} / \text{lot}$$

2) If you divide after the consonant, the vowel is short:

$$\text{prĕs} / \text{ent}$$

 it:

fever or diver?

minute or minus?

blushes or blemish?

salad or solid?

rapids or radish?

banker or baker?

planter or planet?

level or liver?

	Spell:		Write:
1.	pla plan	ent et	_____
2.	min mi	ute nus	_____
3.	rel rol	ick ish	_____
4.	si sil	lent late	_____
5.	rap rag	ide ids	_____
5.	sliv sil	er ent	_____
7.	ran ra	zor ven	_____

Yes or No?

	Yes No
1. Do you put relish on a hot dog?	☐ ☐
2. Would a raven make a good pilot?	☐ ☐
3. Is a diver a rapid swimmer?	☐ ☐
4. Will you cry if you have a sliver in your finger?	☐ ☐
5. Have you ever been to the planet Venus?	☐ ☐
6. Do you like waving to trucks as you ride by?	☐ ☐
7. Is it fun baking a cake as a present for a pal?	☐ ☐

To help read these words, think of the rules to divide words into syllables.

◯ the word to match the picture:

	prison prevent present		sofa solo soda
	silent silken sliver		total pillow pilot
	relax relish relent		raven ravish naval
	primer preside prison		Chinese chapel chopper

Pick the best word to finish each sentence:

raven	prison	present
silent	minus	chapel
relish	pilot	rapid

1. When you grow up, you may be a _____ and fly a jet.

2. If you can be _____ when you hide, you may win at hide-and-seek.

3. They like to grill hot dogs and put _____ on them.

4. If she robs a bank, she may go to _____.

5. A _____ is black like a crow and can fly.

6. It is fun to get a _____ in the mail.

7. You may get the prize if you are a _____ runner.

"X" it:

1. The diver got a lobster stuck in his mask. ☐

   The lobster is diving deeper into the reef. ☐

2. The raven flaps its wings when it visits the prison. ☐

   Rachel's raven-black hair blows in the silent wind. ☐

3. Jason needs a level cup of milk for his baking. ☐

   Waving her helmet, the pilot lands on the planet. ☐

4. Lin got a sliver in her finger chopping the tree. ☐

   The silver ring on Lin's finger was a present. ☐

5. Ten minus three is seven. ☐

   Ten-three-seven are my padlock numbers. ☐

6. The king's wedding was held in the silver chapel. ☐

   That chap had his wedding on a sand dune. ☐

7. Rufus has a blemish on his nose. ☐

   Rufus likes relish on his hot dog bun. ☐

Write it:

1. _____

2. _____

3. _____

4. _____

5. _____

6. _____

7. _____

Lesson 5

Sometimes a word has a silent-*e* syllable. If it is at the beginning of the word, divide the word after the silent *e*.

rose / bud

Draw a line between the syllables in each word below:

confuse	volume
vampire	homesick
compete	stampede
pavement	locate
provide	suppose

Read, write, and "X" it:

1.	tadpole _____			
2.	erase _____			
3.	polite _____			
4.	umpire _____			
5.	rosebud _____			
6.	campsite _____			
7.	classmate _____			

Sometimes a word has a silent-**e** syllable.

rose / bud

◯ it:

 fireside or firehose?	 program or profile?
 trombone or backbone?	 rotate or reptile?
 combine or collide?	 bedside or bagpipe?
 flagpole or tadpole?	 compute or compare?

		Spell:		Write:
1.		tom trom	bane bone	_____
2.		cap camp	site sile	_____
3.	3+2=5 3+4=6 4+3=7 5+2=7 9−1=8 6+2=8	mis nes	tape take	_____
4.		rose nose	dub bud	_____
5.		ex es	cape plode	_____
6.		ban pan	cape cake	_____
7.		in un	side dise	_____

Yes or No?

	Yes No
1. If you make a mistake on the trapeze, can you erase it?	☐ ☐
2. Would you put rosebuds inside a closet?	☐ ☐
3. Can you have a bonfire at your campsite?	☐ ☐
4. Is it polite to explode when the umpire calls a strike?	☐ ☐
5. Is it fun to eat pancakes by a campfire at sunrise?	☐ ☐
6. Will a hero use a bagpipe to put out a fire?	☐ ☐
7. Can a tadpole slide down the fire escape?	☐ ☐

To help read these words, think of the rules to divide words into syllables.

◯ the word to match the picture:

	effect erase irate		endear escape estate
	explore explode exit		dogtag backbone bagpipe
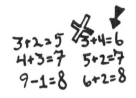	mistake mistreat mister		panel cake pan pancake
	inside invite insole		unrest sunrise unwise

Pick the best word to finish each sentence:

campsite	trombone	polite
mistake	sunrise	trapeze
pancakes	tadpole	umpire

1. It is fun to flip _____ and eat them with bacon.

2. If you shake hands and say "thank you," you are _____.

3. I will relax in my tent at the lakeside _____.

4. A _____ has a long tail and will grow into a frog.

5. Mabel must use a ladder to reach the _____.

6. At the baseball game the _____ will say "strike!"

7. The band makes fine music when LuAnn plays the _____.

"X" it:

1. The tadpole thinks the reptile is handsome and polite. ☐

   The reptile is the pilot of the big river boat. ☐

2. The vampire puts out the fire at the campsite. ☐

   The camper hides the bagpipes by the campfire. ☐

3. My classmate makes a mistake when he computes. ☐

   My classmate makes a mistake when he sits on the cactus. ☐

4. The rosebud begins to open at sunrise. ☐

   At sunrise the trombone begins to blast. ☐

5. The umpire is inside the bullpen. ☐

   The bullet explodes inside the pistol. ☐

6. Jasper likes to catch tadpoles and put them in a bucket. ☐

   Jasper likes to play table tennis. ☐

7. Max Devine gets twisted on the trapeze. ☐

   The trapeze may collide with an airplane. ☐

Write it:

1. _____

   _____

2. $3+2=5$ $5+4=6$

   $4+3=7$ $5+2=7$

   $9-1=8$ $6+2=8$

   _____

3. _____

   _____

4. _____

   _____

5. _____

   _____

6. _____

   _____

7. _____

   _____

Lesson 6

Sometimes 2 vowels together in a syllable make 1 sound. This is a vowel digraph syllable: *ai, ay, ee, ea, oa, ow.* The sound is the long sound of the first vowel.

r**ow** / b**oa**t

○ the vowel digraph syllables in the words below.

beneath	playtime
painless	hollow
appear	peacock
regain	steamboat
showcase	yellow

Read, write, and "X" it:

1.	shadow _____			
2.	playmate _____			
3.	teapot _____			
4.	sneakers _____			
5.	pillow _____			
6.	driveway _____			
7.	stairway _____			

Sometimes 2 vowels together in a syllable make 1 sound.
This is a vowel digraph syllable: *ai, ay, ee, ea, oa, ow.*

r<u>ow</u> / b<u>oa</u>t

◯ it:

teapot or tepee?

toaster or soapsuds?

shipboard or skateboard?

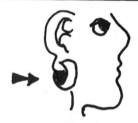

earring or eating?

cotton or coffee?

speaking or sneakers?

beaver or beacon?

peacock or peanut?

1. | rail | rain | coat | cot | _____

2. | six | sik | ten | teen | _____

3. | bil | pil | lay | low | _____

4. | nail | mail | box | book | _____

5. | Sun | Run | day | way | _____

6. | pai | pea | tun | nut | _____

7. | shap | shad | ode | ow | _____

Yes or No?

	Yes	No
1. Do you get letters in the mailbox on Sunday?	☐	☐
2. Should you fill a teapot with soapsuds?	☐	☐
3. Will you put on your raincoat when you are diving?	☐	☐
4. Will you and a playmate run up a wide stairway?	☐	☐
5. Can you feel a peanut that is under your pillow?	☐	☐
6. When you get in a sailboat, do you put on sneakers?	☐	☐
7. Do you feel as if you are flying when you jump off a stairway?	☐	☐

To help read these words, think of the rules to divide words into syllables.

◯  the word to match the picture:

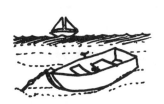 pillar elbow pillow	 mealtime maiden mailbox
 stickpin sixteen seating	 steering strainer stairway
 rowboat roadblock roaring	 tepee teapot tearful
 playback playmate playpen	 spearmint speechless speedboat

Pick the best word to finish each sentence:

teapot	oatmeal	raincoat
peanuts	Sunday	speedboat
pillow	sneakers	shadow

1. It is fun to take a fast ride in a _____.

2. You should have _____ on your feet to play tennis.

3. If it rains, a _____ can keep you dry.

4. When the sun shines, the tree has a long _____.

5. _____ comes at the end of the weekend.

6. At the baseball game it is fun to eat _____.

7. A green blanket and a soft _____ are on my bed.

"X" it:

1. The tepee casts a long shadow at sunset. ☐

   The teapot steams and sings at teatime. ☐

2. The speedboat leaves a trail of soapsuds. ☐

   The beaver drives the speedboat with its tail. ☐

3. Mabel slides on the stairway rail with a pillow. ☐

   The driver stares at the skunk hidden in Nina's raincoat. ☐

4. The umpire heats a teapot at the ball game. ☐

   The umpire heats oatmeal at the campsite. ☐

5. Mona has lots of soapsuds in her coffee. ☐

   Milo is spilling coffee all over his raincoat. ☐

6. My playmate lost her earring at the Snow Bowl. ☐

   My dad's rowboat is on a trailer in the hallway. ☐

7. Pedro is happy to be sixteen years old at last. ☐

   On Sunday six teens played soccer. ☐

Write it:

1. _____

2. _____

3. _____

4. _____

5. _____

6. _____

7. _____

Lesson 7

When a word has 3 consonants that come between 2 vowels, you must look carefully for a **consonant blend** or a **consonant digraph**. The blend or digraph will stay together as part of a syllable.

hun / dred

◯ the blend or digraph. Then draw a line between the syllables in each word below.

impress	hamster
chitchat	instep
reckless	crackpot
backlash	sandman
misspell	unstuck

Read, write, and "X" it:

1.	dustpan _____			
2.	inspect _____			
3.	pumpkin _____			
4.	nostril _____			
5.	tantrum _____			
6.	chopsticks _____			
7.	kingdom _____			

When a word has 3 consonants that come between 2 vowels, you must look carefully for a consonant blend or a consonant digraph. The blend or digraph will stay together as part of a syllable.

◯ it: **hun / dred**

handling   or   antlers?

mustang   or   mattress?

ticklish   or   stickpin?

distress   or   dishrag?

shoplift   or   chopsticks?

handcuff   or   handbag?

snapshot   or   gunshot?

ketchup   or   ostrich?

	Spell:			Write:
1.	dump	pump	ling	kin	_____
2.	sub	bus	tract	trot	_____
3.	lad	lob	der	ster	_____
4.	tin	tan	trum	drum	_____
5.	nos	sun	trail	tril	_____
6.	sent	sand	wick	wich	_____
7.	bang	king	dom	gun	_____

Yes or No?

	Yes No
1. Can you cut a smile on a pumpkin with chopsticks?	☐ ☐
2. Does a panther have antlers and a striped tail?	☐ ☐
3. Will an actress pose while you take a snapshot?	☐ ☐
4. Is a lobster ticklish under its nostrils?	☐ ☐
5. Would you dust your nose with a dustpan and wipe it with a dishrag?	☐ ☐
6. Will your parents be upset if you jump and dive on the best mattress?	☐ ☐
7. Would you have a tantrum if I put a lobster in your handbag?	☐ ☐

To help read these words, think of the rules to divide words into syllables.

◯ the word to match the picture:

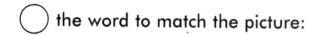

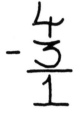

stumble
support
subtract

sandman
sandwich
Spanish

dustpan
dishcloth
bluster

endless
atlas
actress

huntress
hundred
hunger

panther
banner
planter

matter
nuthatch
mattress

kingdom
ketchup
kitchen

Pick the best word to finish each sentence:

chopsticks	kingdom	panther
sandwich	actress	tantrum
mattress	dishpan	pumpkin

1. If you cut a nose and a grin in a _____, you will have a jack-o'-lantern.

2. When you get mad and cry and stamp your feet, you have a _____.

3. A bed has springs and a _____.

4. In the tale, the king and queen live in a vast _____.

5. Sally Davis was the best _____ in the play.

6. On the picnic we each had a bag of chips and a _____ to eat.

7. Jason lets the dishes soak in the _____.

"X" it:

1. A hundred pumpkins are growing in the kingdom. ☐

   The pumpkin became a silver coach fit for a queen. ☐

2. The ostrich ate Chester's ham and cheese sandwich. ☐

   Chester had a tantrum when his sandbox was broken. ☐

3. The buck has its antlers stuck in my handbag. ☐

   The duck put handcuffs on the deer's antlers. ☐

4. Brave Hilda began to unload the lobster pots. ☐

   "I am so hot," said the lobster, springing from the pot. ☐

5. "Something in this mattress makes me feel ticklish," said Fido. ☐

   Matt thinks Fido is ticklish under his chin. ☐

6. The panther puts on a Scotch kilt when it plays the bagpipes. ☐

   The person inspecting the pipes pulls Scotch tape from his pocket. ☐

7. The actress likes to hear cheering and hundreds of hands clapping. ☐

   The endless cheering helped the team push the score to a hundred. ☐

Write it:

1. _____

2. _____

3. _____

4. _____

5. _____

6. _____

7. _____

Lesson 8

When you divide a word into syllables, be sure to keep blends and digraphs together.

sun / shine   **rain / drop**

◯ the blend or digraph and draw a line between the syllables.

complete	steamship
soapstone	lobster
include	wishbone
concrete	teamster
backside	upgrade

Read, write, and "X" it:

1.	roadblock _____			
2.	unbraid _____			
3.	athlete _____			
4.	complain _____			CHICKEN NO REFUNDS
5.	daydream _____			
6.	nickname _____	Jack Sanderson		90
7.	bathrobe _____			

When you divide a word into syllables, be sure to keep blends and digraphs together.

sunshine   **raindrop**

 it:

showboat or snowflake?

unrest or undress?

toasting or coastline?

backbone or duckbill?

weekday or wheelchair?

unclean or reclaim?

CHICKEN
NO REFUNDS

contain or complain?

milkweed or misspell?

	Spell:		Write:
1.	leap lap	frog fog	_____
2.	bay day	dream dram	_____
3.	mick nick	home name	_____
4.	ath ash	lete let	_____
5.	ran rain	drop prod	_____
6.	hand had	rail trail	_____
7.	bathe bath	rob robe	_____

Yes or No?

	Yes	No
1. Do you like your own nickname?	☐	☐
2. Would a milkshake made of milkweed and raindrops taste good?	☐	☐
3. Can a real frozen snowflake be homemade?	☐	☐
4. Do you daydream of being a super athlete?	☐	☐
5. Is a leapfrog a kind of reptile?	☐	☐
6. Would you complain if we had sunshine all the time?	☐	☐
7. If you twist your backbone, will you need a wheelchair?	☐	☐

To help read these words, think of the rules to divide words into syllables.

◯ the word to match the picture:

	leaflet leafless leapfrog		backward backbone backstop
	unless undress unstuck		stunning sunshine runway
	antler asleep athlete		railroad raindrop rainbow
	cobweb cockroach cockpit		hammock handcuff handmade

Pick the best word to finish each sentence:

handmade	nickname	daydream
backbone	athlete	leapfrog
raindrop	unbraids	handrail

1. His granddad likes a gift that is _____.

2. My pals like to jump and play_____ on the grass.

3. Lee is a fine_____ and helps win the football game.

4. If the steps are steep, you can grab the _____.

5. After a swim, Freda _____ her hair, brushes it, and lets it dry.

6. It is fun to relax on the grass and _____.

7. Her name is Susan, but Sue is her_____.

"X" it:

1.
Ivan complains of a pain in his backbone. ☐

It is plain that a cactus has no backbone! ☐

2.
Lulu spends her nickel at the drugstore. ☐

Lulu named her new rowboat "Nickel." ☐

3.
Ramon includes Rocko in the Sunday dinner. ☐

Rocko takes a steamboat trip to East Hampton. ☐

4.
The wise athlete must complete the Latin exam. ☐

The boastful athlete will compete for the grandest prize. ☐

5.
Winston plays leapfrog with the handbag. ☐

The frog leaped over the handrail and landed on Winston. ☐

6.
As Thelma daydreams, an oak leaf falls into her milkshake. ☐

It is a mistake for Thelma to daydream of cupcakes and donuts in class. ☐

7.
Wilma unbraids her long hair and gathers it in a ribbon. ☐

Wilma unbraids the ribbons on her long, satin bathrobe. ☐

Write it:

1. _____

2. _____

3. _____

4. _____

5. _____

6. _____

7. _____

Lesson 9

When a 2-syllable word ends in y, the y says /ē/. The y takes the consonant before it to make the last syllable.

pen / ny

Draw a line between the syllables:

silly	bony
Betsy	creamy
slimy	pansy
dusty	bulky
daily	gravy

Read, write, and "X" it:

1. **messy** _____			
2. **smoky** _____			
3. **frisky** _____			
4. **rainy** _____			
5. **sixty** _____			
6. **shiny** _____			
7. **sleepy** _____			

When a 2-syllable word ends in y, the y says /ē/. The y takes the consonant before it to make the last syllable.

pen / ny

 it:

bunny or bumpy?

smoky or snaky?

shaky or shady?

stuffy or sloppy?

baggy or Patsy?

ring or ratty?

shiny or shady?

misty or sixty?

			Write:
1.	mes mus	sy ky	_____
2.	sow slow	ly gly	_____
3.	fan fun	my ny	_____
4.	nine nin	try ty	_____
5.	sha shab	dy by	_____
6.	can skin	ny dy	_____
7.	lad la	by dy	_____

Yes or No?

	Yes No
1. Would a penny buy sixty sticks of candy?	☐ ☐
2. Do you get angry when a big, frisky puppy jumps on you?	☐ ☐
3. Can a skinny pony be plump?	☐ ☐
4. If you are ninety years old, are you just a kid?	☐ ☐
5. Would a smoky kitchen make you sneeze?	☐ ☐
6. Do you move slowly when you are sleepy?	☐ ☐
7. Can a weeping willow tree really weep?	☐ ☐

To help read these words, think of the rules to divide words into syllables.

◯ the word to match the picture:

nineteen
nasty
ninety

pansy
penny
pony

lazy
landing
lady

funny
bony
tummy

navy
rainy
nearest

antlers
angry
annual

slinky
sixty
misty

sleepy
flaky
creepy

Pick the best word to finish each sentence:

shady	frisky	skinny
slowly	rainy	smoky
messy	Henry	sleepy

1.

Hank is one of the nicknames for _____.

2.

It is wise to go to bed when you feel _____.

3.

The rug was _____ after the puppy spilled the can of paint on it.

4.

If you feel hot in the summer, sit in a _____ spot under a tree.

5.

That pony likes to gallop and act very _____.

6.

If the wind blows near the grill, the fire may get

_____.

7.

The sun rarely shines on a _____ day.

"X" it:

1.
Patsy is a sloppy eater and drinker. ☐

Patsy the dragon eats paste and drinks fire. ☐

2.
Lucky Henry has a shiny red wagon. ☐

Henry is wagging his shiny red tail. ☐

3.
Bozo has a bumpy nose and funny reddish hair. ☐

The funny red radish is long, skinny, and bumpy. ☐

4.
The messy pigs play leapfrog on a rainy day. ☐

The sleepy pigs complain to the skinny reptile. ☐

5.
Dobbin, my pony, is sloppy when he eats his dinner. ☐

The sloppy waiter makes the diners quite messy. ☐

6.
It was so rainy that Ricky jogged in his swimming trunks. ☐

Ramon is swinging from the end of a shiny rainbow. ☐

7.
Lilly became sleepy reading under the leafy tree. ☐

The weeping willow tree is angry that it cannot weep. ☐

Write it:

1. 60 _____

2. _____

3. _____

4. _____

5. _____

6. 90 _____

7. _____

When -*le* is at the end of a word, it takes the consonant before it to make the last syllable.

cat / tle

Draw a line between the syllables:

crumble	battle
title	trample
gamble	maple
feeble	simple
smuggle	twinkle

Read, write, and "X" it:

1.	thimble _____			
2.	table _____			
3.	bundle _____			
4.	puddle _____			
5.	needle _____			
6.	bridle _____			
7.	stumble _____			

When -*le* is at the end of a word, it takes the consonant before it to make the last syllable.

cat / tle

◯ it:

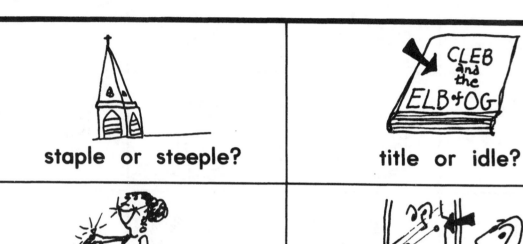

staple or steeple?

title or idle?

saddle or dazzle?

simple or pimple?

giggle or jungle?

maple or staple?

dangle or ankle?

bundle or fumble?

1. ta   fa   dle   ble   _____

2. pum   dim   ple   ble   _____

3. im   an   gle   kle   _____

4. fid   fib   dle   tle   _____

5. stee   stum   ble   ple   _____

6. sat   sta   tle   ble   _____

7. nib   nip   ble   gle   _____

Yes or No?

	Yes	No
1. Do cattle nibble grass in the summer?	☐	☐
2. If you stumble on the path, will you giggle?	☐	☐
3. Can you mend a hole in a kettle with a needle and thimble?	☐	☐
4. Could you put a bridle on a pony in the stable?	☐	☐
5. Can you twist your ankle when you jump over a puddle?	☐	☐
6. Would it be easy to put an apple on the top of a steeple?	☐	☐
7. Is a dimple the same as a pimple?	☐	☐

To help read these words, think of the rules to divide words into syllables.

○ the word to match the picture:

steeple
stumble
stable

tingle
little
title

saddle
cattle
rattle

kettle
kitten
settle

noble
needle
beetle

fibber
table
fiddle

stable
sample
stabbing

puddle
paddle
bugle

Pick the best word to finish each sentence:

bridle	needle	title
nibble	bundle	fiddle
ankle	kettle	cattle

1. She can play music on the _____.

2. You can use a _____ to help fix a rip.

3. I heat water in a _____ on the stove.

4. Ann rides the pony with a saddle and a _____.

5. Your _____ may swell if you fall and twist it.

6. In the pasture I can see sheep and _____.

7. All of the letters in the mailbox are in a _____.

"X" it:

1.
The cattle are drinking from a puddle. ☐

Robin likes to drink pudding from the kettle. ☐

2.
Tony is playing the fiddle at the table. ☐

Tony fiddles with his program during the play. ☐

3.
The tiny flea nibbles at Mona's ankle. ☐

Mona nibbles on soggy crackers and cheese. ☐

4.
The pony gets a bundle of hay in the stable. ☐

The camels take the bundles to the stable. ☐

5.
Rudy puts the brass ashtray on the table. ☐

Ruby puts the dusty ashcan on the table. ☐

6.
Betty smuggles secrets to the navy. ☐

Betty snuggles into the soft, navy sofa. ☐

7.
Ricky giggles as he begins to read his simple lines. ☐

Ricky cannot juggle a single apple with a peach. ☐

Write it:

1. _____

2. _____

3. _____

4. _____

5. _____

6. _____

7. _____

Using the rules you have learned, draw a line between the syllables in each word below.

bad / min / ton

Atlantic	educate
chickadee	president
rapidly	fiddlesticks
attendant	Mexico
molasses	republic

Read, write, and "X" it:

1.	monument _____			
2.	buttonhole _____			
3.	jellyfish _____			DING DONG
4.	consonants _____			zpcfg thbx
5.	refreshment _____			
6.	microscope _____		3+2=5 3+4=6 4+3=7 5+2=7 9-1=8 6+2=8	
7.	wintertime _____			

92

Remember the rules for dividing words into syllables.

bad / min / ton

$\bigcirc$ it:

storekeeper or stonecutter?

unbraided or umbrella?

evergreen or volunteer?

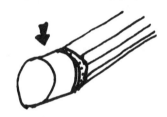

propeller or eraser?

eleven or elastic?

suddenly or sunbathing?

confident or monument?

pineapple or penmanship?

	Spell:			Write:
1. *11*	e al	lev le	en wen	_____
2. zpcfg thbx	con co	so con	ex nants	_____
3.	pin pine	ip ap	ple ble	_____
4.	win wi	ter der	tim time	_____
5.	bag bad	min mut	ton tone	_____
6.	but bu	ton gun	hole hall	_____
7.	le lem	none on	ade ad	_____

Yes or No?

		Yes	No
1.	Is it fun to play badminton with an athlete?	☐	☐
2.	Do you get vitamins from your daily meals?	☐	☐
3.	Are there seven consonants in *peppermint*?	☐	☐
4.	Will you discover a jellyfish while skating in the wintertime?	☐	☐
5.	If you are sunbathing, are you beginning to get a tan?	☐	☐
6.	Would you volunteer to clean the erasers?	☐	☐
7.	Do you make lemonade with a pineapple?	☐	☐

To help read these words, think of the rules to divide words into syllables.

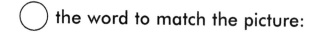 the word to match the picture:

commander
commenting
continent

summertime
seventeen
suddenly

pillowcase
pickpocket
pineapple

volunteer
venison
volcano

president
peppermint
popular

probably
propeller
provided

lemonade
melody
paperback

backgammon
banister
badminton

Pick the best word to finish each sentence:

lemonade	wintertime	volunteer
consonants	peppermint	continent
jellyfish	microscope	buttonhole

1. The letters, not including **a**, **e**, **i**, **o**, and **u** are called
_____.

2. With a globe you can study each sea and each
_____.

3. A _____ will make a tiny thing seem
big.

4. Do you like to make snowmen or ride on a sled in the
_____?

5. On a jacket each button fits in a _____.

6. After I mow the grass and get hot, I drink some
_____.

7. A stick of red and white candy may taste of
_____.

"X" it:

1. The inventor is poking his finger into his sneaker. ☐

   The insect is sneaking under the broken microscope. ☐

2. The jellyfish is sunbathing on the sandy beach. ☐

   The clever sunfish is making beach plum jelly. ☐

3. A dozen pineapples doze under a shiny umbrella. ☐

   Pamela does not understand that pineapples do not make lemonade. ☐

4. The propeller on the small plane is quite shaky. ☐

   The shaky glider has no propeller. ☐

5. Seventeen pupils volunteer to clean the erasers. ☐

   The pupils see the volcano erupt seventeen times. ☐

6. Felix has a chocolate hat and a peppermint cane. ☐

   Felix bakes a chocolate cake with peppermint frosting. ☐

7. The band stopped to salute at the monument. ☐

   The bandit traveled across the frozen continent. ☐

Write it:

1. _____

2. _____

3. _____

4. _____

5. _____

6. _____

7. _____

Book 4½ — Posttest

(Teacher dictated. See Key for Books 1 to 5.)

◯ the word you hear.

1. slipper silver sliver silken	2. animal actress antlers athlete
3. compare complain compact compute	4. bunchy bumpy dumpy dusty
5. crabbed crayon crater credit	6. robot relate rotate rebate
7. sample simple ramble sandal	8. profits frolics tropics trapeze
9. propeller professor prosecute protector	10. volume valentine volunteer voluntary

Book 4½ — Posttest

(Teacher dictated. See Key for Books 1 to 5.)

1. _____

_____

2. _____

_____

3. _____

_____

4. _____

_____

5. _____

_____

Book 4½ — Posttest

Using the rules you have learned, put a line between the syllables in the words below, and mark the vowel in the first syllable long or short.

relax	railroad	tempest	helpful
crazy	dictate	fellow	crackpot
title	begin	madness	infect
thimble	hamster	sprinkle	minus
ugly	distress	spinach	mistake
choppy	driveway	insult	sunrise
basin	riddle	reason	relish
public	profit	belong	weekend
rainbow	holy	tantrum	finish
stampede	fable	beneath	handful
suspend	comic	nostril	locate

Book 4½ — Posttest

Use the words to complete the sentences.

athlete   sneakers   ankle   slowly
puddle   bundle   rainy   relax

1. If you can jog five miles, you are a real
   _____. You don't need much
   equipment, but you do need _____
   that fit well. You begin by running
   _____ and then you go faster. Even if
   it is snowy or _____, you keep on
   running. But do not splash in a _____!
   Remember that when you get home you can sit
   and _____.

teapot   raindrops   table   pineapple
chopsticks   menu   ticklish   China

2. When we go out for a Chinese dinner, we sit at a
   _____ and read the
   _____. We select chicken with
   _____ and lobster with peapods. We
   eat the meal with _____. The waiter
   brings a _____ filled with hot tea.
   Would it be fun to live in _____ and
   eat this way every day?

Go on to the next page.

stingray   butterfly   sea   erase

ashtray   rowboat   diver   appears

3. Molly is rowing on the _____ when she sees a dragonfly. As she takes her _____ net to try to catch it, she tumbles from the _____ into the water. The shadows of the seaweed scare Molly. "Will I be attacked by a _____ or a jellyfish?" she wonders, but no sea monster_____. Molly swims safely to shore, and then she tells her dad, "I will never be an undersea _____."